The fish dish

Sheila Blackburn

National Literacy Strategy
Encourage your child to recognize these essential words
as you read this story:

but did do don't down good had have home
make man must next not one   some that them
three want what with your

Clever Cat was in the kitchen. She had to make some lunch.

"What can I make for lunch?" said
Clever Cat.

"That fish dish looks good. I can make that," said Clever Cat.

Clever Cat made a list. She had to get some fresh fish.

Clever Cat went to the fish shop, but the shop was shut!

"What can I do?" said Clever Cat.
"I must get some fresh fish for lunch."

Clever Cat went to the next shop.
"I don't sell fish," said the man.

Clever Cat went to the next shop.
No fresh fish!

Clever Cat went to three shops. Not one had fresh fish.

Clever Cat went home. She did not
see Firefighter Fred.

Fred did not see Clever Cat. Crash!
Bump! Fred sat down with a thump.

"Sorry, Fred," said Clever Cat.
"Is this your bag?"

"Yes, it's three fresh fish. Do you want them?" said Fred.

"Fresh fish! Oh yes," said Clever Cat.
Did you catch them?"

"Thank you Fred. Come and have lunch with Lucy and me!" said Clever Cat.

Who can run the fastest?

Lucy Lind

National Literacy Strategy
Encourage your child to recognize these essential words
as you read this story:

ball but by do has help him just not now off
over put so some than that then too us very
want what who will

"I can run fast. I bet I can run faster than you!" says Bouncy Ben to Clever Cat.

"Yes, you can run fast, but I can run fast too," says Clever Cat.

"I can run fast," says Dippy Duck.

"So can I," says Peter Puppy.

"Let's put it to the test," says Clever Cat.

"Let's see who can run the fastest!"

"Do you want to run, Eddy Elephant?"
says Dippy Duck.

"I'm big and strong, but I'm not very fast," says Eddy. "I'll just run for fun."

"Munching Mike, will you help to set us off?" says Clever Cat.

Mike puts some string on the grass.

"Step up to the string," he says.

Off they go! Bouncy Ben soon springs
to the front.

Then Ben gets stuck in the mud. Now Peter Puppy has sped past him.

Peter Puppy trips over a stump. Now Clever Cat and Eddy are neck and neck.

Will Eddy win by a trunk? Who**osh!**
A ball of wind and dust whizzes past.

It sets Dippy Duck in a spin.

"What was that?" says Dippy Duck.

"We forgot Zig Zag Zebra!" says
Eddy Elephant.

"We forgot that Zig Zag Zebra can run faster than all of us!" says Clever Cat.